Postcard from Morocco

music by Argento

text by ...ahue

Boosey and Hawkes

POSTCARD FROM MOROCCO

An Opera

music by
DOMINICK ARGENTO

text by
JOHN DONAHUE

BOOSEY & HAWKES

Commissioned by

THE CENTER OPERA ASSOCIATION

for

THE CENTER OPERA COMPANY

Dedicated to

ALICE and JUSTIN V. SMITH

whose efforts and generosity have made Center Opera possible

POSTCARD FROM MOROCCO

The scene must present a distinctly off or odd angle as indeed the whole of the piece must, but not morbid or peculiar so much as wacky or exotic, sometimes romantic and also like a memory (1914), like an old postcard from a foreign land showing a railway station of Morocco or someplace, hot, strange, etc., but then translated through the eyes of a designer into a semi-cartoon-like atmosphere. The railway station should also be like the interior of a glass-covered pavilion or conservatory, restaurant, waiting area, spa.

There are entertainments present, cardboard vendors, and waiters of tables, a curious daytime floorshow for the benefit of the train-waiting guests; a kind of play, a puppet play (but done with very human-like puppets) which is performed on a small covered stage at one end or at the side of the room. Around this place of waiting are scattered the people. Some are real and some are not. Several move about on small wheels with cords which allow them to be pulled back and forth or perhaps they just turn or jerk in position slightly.

The decor is false but charming; potted cardboard ferns, and benches of cardboard, glass around and overhead. Accompanying this little comedy is an Algerian orchestra which is ever present in costume and fez and seen through some cardboard ferns. They provide music for all the little eating, watching, dancing and various other *divertissements* that take place throughout. By the look on their faces they seem to have seen it all before and will see it again.

The live characters play more than one role, snatching from time to time the special half-masks off others in the station whenever a new character must appear. These may 'come alive' and 'go dead' at will. We see each one trying hard to protect whatever small part of himself he has in his suitcase, the symbol of his secret or lack of secret, his dream or lack of dream. It is through the false fabric woven by the waiting creatures as the piece progresses that we see our own fears and anxieties rendered along with the fierce way in which man protects himself from the stranger, his probing wish for company and comfort, his own fears. The ultimate defense for this group is to discover a waiting creature vulnerable enough to reveal the real contents of his suitcase.

In presenting this piece, one must see to it that what is really happening does not seem to be occurring at all; an innocent, curious silliness, which only in retrospect remembers pain. Curious, foreign, remembered, comic, childish and playful, dreamlike, and viewed down a long hall are the desirable qualities.

Poor Mr. Owen . . . if only he could have gotten a look into someone else's suitcase . . . ? ? ? ? ?

John Donahue

CAST

Coloratura-soprano ....A Lady with a Hand Mirror
An Operetta Singer

Soprano ....A Lady with a Cake Box

Mezzo-soprano .... A Lady with a Hat Box
A Foreign Singer

Lyric Tenor..A Man with Old Luggage
First Puppet
An Operetta Singer

Tenor .... A Man with a Paint Box

Baritone ....A Man with a Shoe Sample Kit
Second Puppet

Bass ....A Man with a Cornet Case
A Puppet Maker

Mimes ....Entertainers

Note

In addition to being the Entertainers during the Divertimento and other live but silent characters at various moments, the Mimes can also impersonate the Puppets, the Operetta Singers, and the dancer during the "Fascination Dance" while the vocal lines are being sung by the singers indicated above.

ORCHESTRA

Clarinet (also Alto Saxophone and Bass Clarinet)
Trombone (bass attachment required)
Classical Guitar (to be amplified acoustically)
Piano/Celesta
Violin   ⎫
Viola   ⎬ soli   (these parts may be doubled)
Double-bass ⎭
Percussion (a set of traps consisting of snare drum, bass drum with foot pedal, tom-toms, sock cymbal, ride cymbal, triangle, temple-blocks, crotales, castanets, E♭ chime, wind chimes, maracas, etc.)

DURATION

Approximately 90 minutes. There is no intermission.

A recording of this work by the Center Opera Company is available on DESTO (DC 7137/38).

WORLD PREMIERE

October 14, 1971

Cedar Village Theatre
Minneapolis, Minnesota

CENTER OPERA COMPANY

Conductor ....Philip Brunelle   Set, Costume Designer ....Jon Barkla

Director ....John Donahue   Lighting Designer ....Carlos Ozols

CAST

Coloratura-soprano ....Sarita Roche

Soprano ....Barbara Brandt

Mezzo-soprano ....Janis Hardy

Lyric Tenor ....Yale Marshall

Tenor ....Vern Sutton

Baritone ....Barry Busse

Bass ....Edward Foreman

Mimes ....Wendy Lehr, Bain Boehlke

ORCHESTRA

Paul Freed, Piano; John Melcher, Percussion; Richard Wyland, Clarinet, Saxophone; Robert Bailey, Trombone; Frederick Sewell, Violin; Alice Preves, Viola; Marie Stacy, Bass; Jeffrey Van, Guitar.

We built a ship upon the stairs . . .

But Tom fell out and hurt his knee,
So there was no one left but me.

(Robert Louis Stevenson)

POSTCARD FROM MOROCCO

Text by
JOHN DONAHUE

Music by
DOMINICK ARGENTO

Andante (♩. = 60-63)

(Pno.)

poco
mp < *sfz*

(A high, shrill train whistle)

(Silence.)

COLORATURA:
ff — *mf*   *dim.*   *pp*

SOPRANO:
ff — *mf*   *dim.*   *pp*
...How

MEZZO:
ff — *mf*   *dim.*   *pp*

LYRIC TENOR:
ff — *mf*   *dim.*   *pp*

TENOR:
ff — *mf*   *dim.*   *pp*

BARITONE:
ff — *mf*   *dim.*   *pp*

BASS:
ff — *mf*   *dim.*   *pp*

mf (Bass)

f   *mp* (pizz.)

(+ Gtr., Bass Dr.)

✻ Indistinct, toneless muttering.

BH. BK. 7.35

Printed in U.S.A.

2

(The lights come up in tiny places to reveal various figures one at a time or in groups. The lights last only a short time on each occasion . . . like little previews.)

4

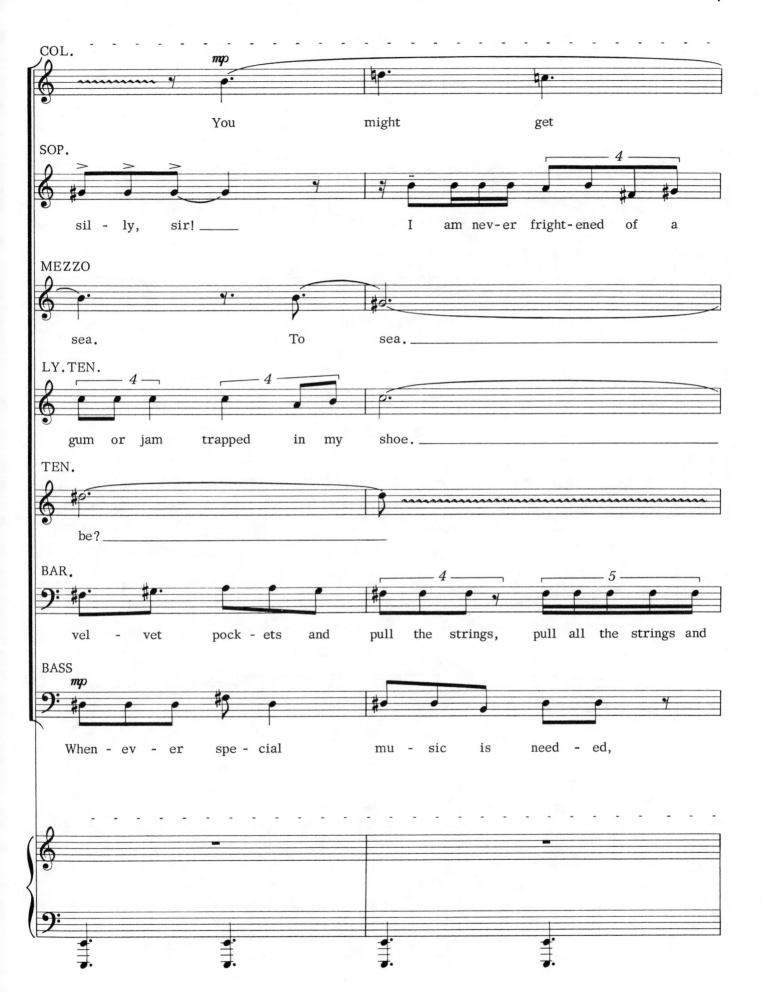

16

(Lights suddenly up to follow the progress of one cardboard figure on wheels cross the stage.)

(It bumps into another figure which we think is also cardboard but which is "real" and comes "alive.")

me, I'm wait-ing ___ for a per - son, ___

my cou - sin, _____ who was a prince. _____

pp misterioso

8- - - - - - - - - -
Ped. _____

mf (whistling)

(Vln. Vla.)

5 Poco meno mosso (♩. = 63)

cupo

He has on a hat.

(quasi gliss.)

18

(The cardboard figure, always wearing an astonished face, moves on.)

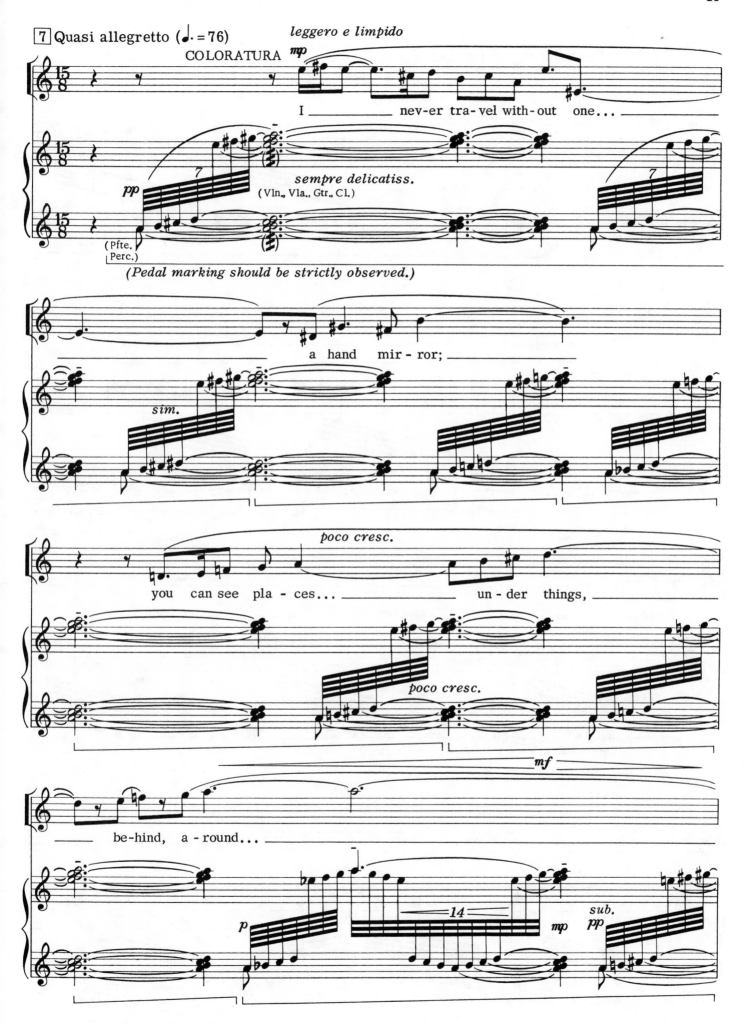

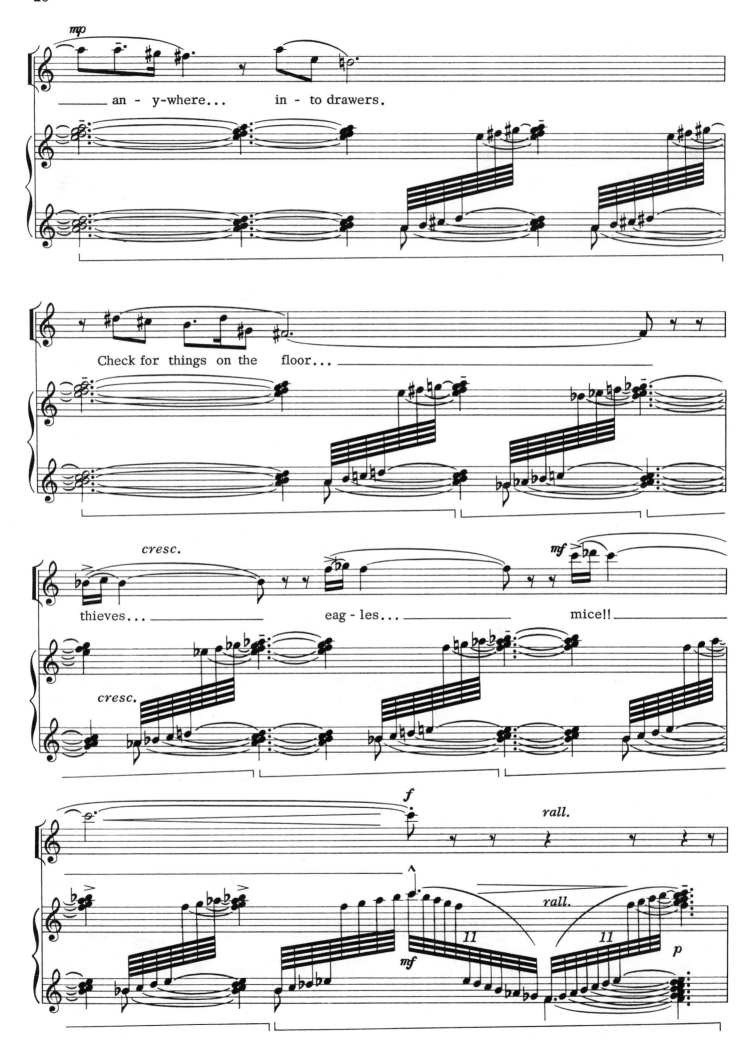

I keep one han - dy --- a hand mir - ror, _____ a hand mir - ror, _____ and _____ fright - en a - way, _____ and _____ fright-en a - way _____ spi - ders _____ and old men with it. _____

They take one look and run a - way.... they take one look and run a - way...

ha, ha, ha, ha, ha, sim.

get too wet...

some - one might see me.

12 Poco più mosso che il principio
($\frac{}{}$ = 63-66)

Some - one might drown me.

SOPRANO

MEZZO

Ahh!

LYRIC TENOR

Ahh!

TENOR

Ahh!

BARITONE

Ahh!

BASS

Ahh!

12 Poco più mosso che il principio
($\frac{}{}$ = 63-66)

accel. come prima

(Now the other cardboard and live people are moving and talking.)

* This ensemble, beginning **p** *sotto voce*, should crescendo until its
conclusion: underscored text in various voices indicates passages
that stand out a bit from the others.

hind, a - round...

She has gone

Low-er it down I said, _____ a lit - tle

see it. _____ I'm lost...

They might steal it and then

sand - bags... ha, ha, ha, ha, ha, ha, ha,

sax - o- phone... you should look me up when-ev - er

cresc.

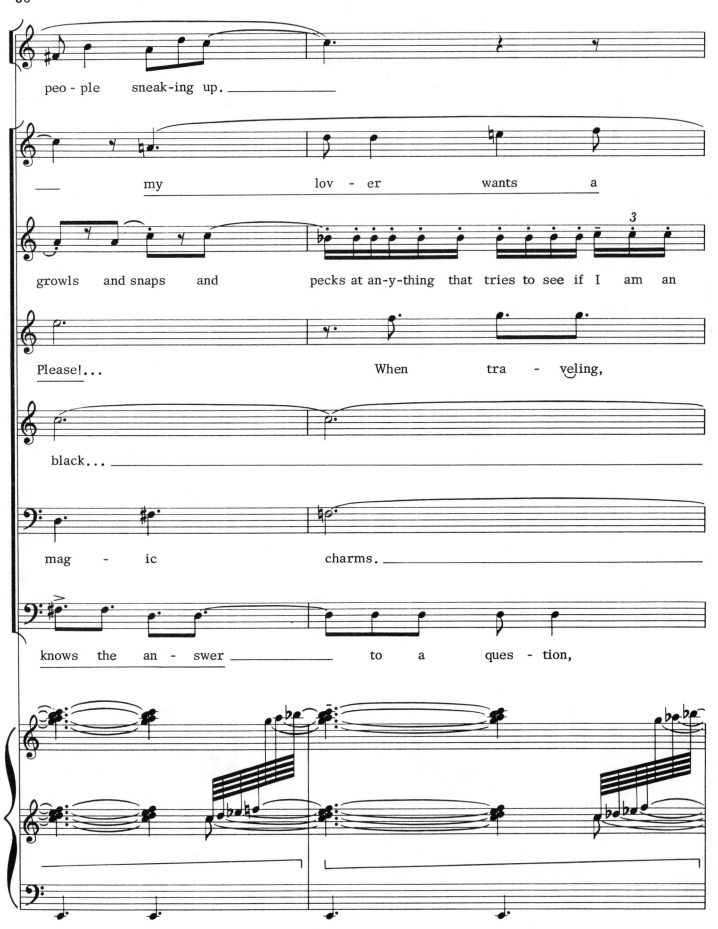

peo - ple sneak-ing up.

my lov - er wants a

growls and snaps and pecks at an-y-thing that tries to see if I am an

Please!... When tra - veling,

black...

mag - ic charms.

knows the an - swer to a ques - tion,

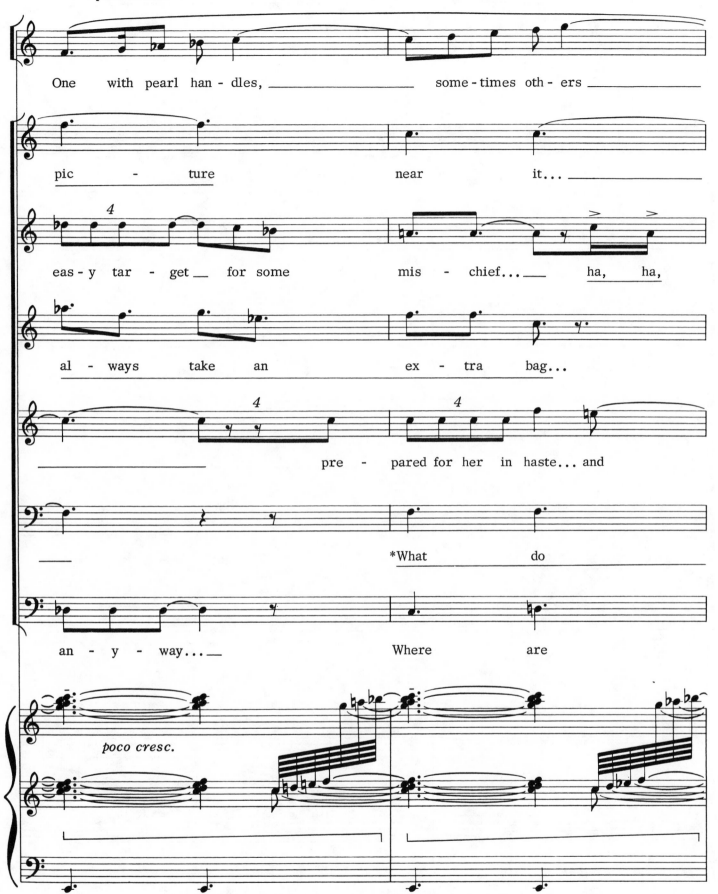

poco cresc.

One with pearl han - dles, _____ some - times oth - ers _____

pic - ture near it... _____

eas - y tar - get _ for some mis - chief... __ ha, ha,

al - ways take an ex - tra bag...

_____ pre - pared for her in haste... and

___ *What do

an - y - way... __ Where are

poco cresc.

* To a young man with a paint box: Mr. Owen.

pock - et, _____ in - side lug - gage tops,

Don't ev - er go with - out one. _____

___ What do you do? _____ What do you do?

good? _____ What do you do? ___ What do

ev-er let an - y - one else touch it! _____ Not for a

you do? _____ What do you do? ___ What do

go - ing? Say, what do ___ you

cresc.

44

(They all freeze.)   *(There is a sudden odd time change, during which we see several different moments*

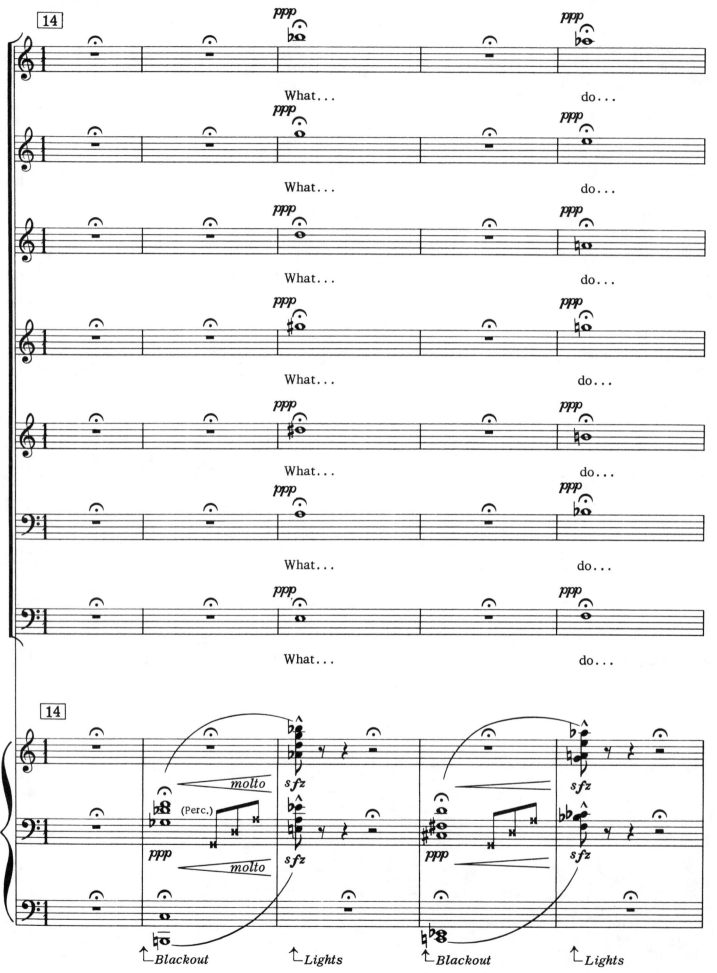

which occurred both before and after this moment in very rapid succession.)

46

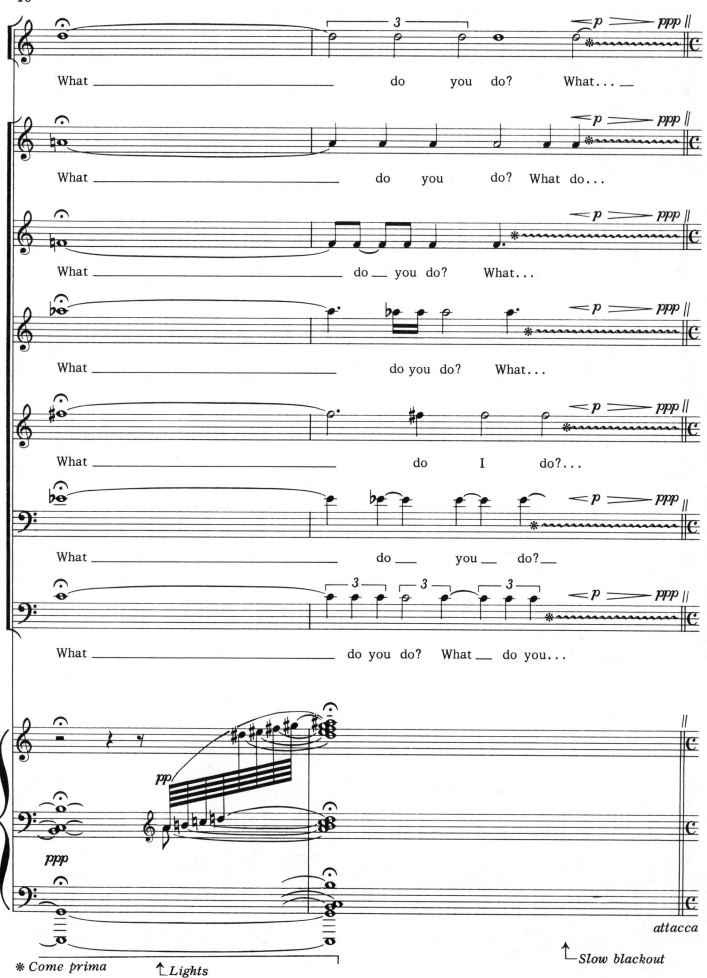

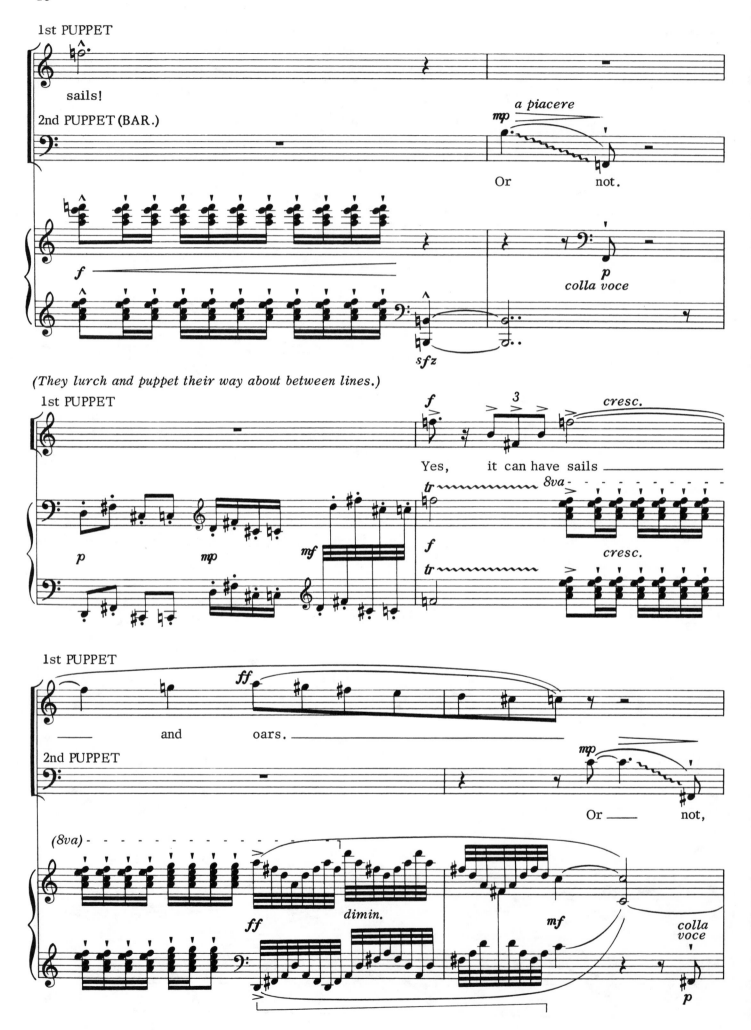

(They lurch and puppet their way about between lines.)

50

1st PUPPET

ff *dimin.* *mf* *rall.* *mp*

right, right, right, right, right, right... if they have one.

(8va)

Meno mosso, misterioso (♩ = 63 ca.)

1st PUPPET

p

This might be an old-er-fash-ioned ship.＿＿＿＿ No, ＿

2nd PUPPET

pp 3

Like a ca-noe?

Meno mosso, misterioso (♩ = 63 ca.)

p

pp

1st PUPPET

mp *f*

like a Vi-king ship ＿ or in Rome... ＿＿＿＿

p *mf*

18 Grazioso e scorrevole (♩. = 66-69)

1st PUPPET

sempre **p**

cloud ship, _____ a ___ cloud ship, _____ more

18 Grazioso e scorrevole (♩. = 66-69)

pp *delicatissimo*

sim.

mag - ic _____ than like a steam - ship. _____

p

1st PUPPET *dimin. a niente*

rall.

Poco meno mosso (♩. = 60)

pp*

A

2nd PUPPET

rall.

pp*

A cloud ship, _____

A

Poco meno mosso (♩. = 60)

poco a poco dimin. e rall.

pp

sognando

* This duettino passage should be done in a quasi-sprechstimme manner.

58

(Beginning at 22 and ending abruptly at 23, the onlookers laugh and punch one another and the watching

dummies, contributing remarks and encouraging the puppets.)

(The puppets cavort around, whacking at one another,
nailing and sawing at the paraphernalia.)

2nd PUPPET

64

sails.   Ah,

sails.   Ah,

sails.   Ah,

sails.   Ah,

sails.   I'd like to

best! You lie, you lie, you lie, you lie, you fool!

best! You lie, you lie, you lie, you lie, you fool!

(8)- - - - - - - - - - - - - - - - - - -

see them   make   a   ship   of   ice   or

Mine's the best ship of   all!

Mine's the best ship of   all!   Mine's the best ship of

(8)-   -   -   -   -   -   -   -   -   -   -   -   -   -

sail!

made of fire... a Fly - ing

made of fire... a Fly - ing

We can build a boat.. made of fire: a Fly - ing

We can build a boat.. made of fire: a Fly - ing

it's the best!

it's the best!

Hoo haa! Wee.

Hoo haa! Wee.

Hoo haa! Wee.

Hoo haa! Wee.

Hoo haa! Wee.

Hoo haa! Wee.

Hoo haa! Wee.

(As one puppet is about to decapitate or smack the other to ruin, the action suspends.)

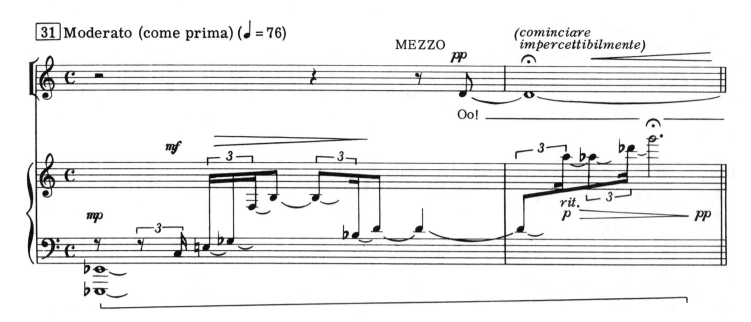

31 Moderato (come prima) (♩ = 76)

(There is an abrupt change in time and we now see the waiting station at an earlier moment before the puppet show has begun. There are few people present. The curtains on the puppet stage are closed and a woman with a microphone is singing. The mood is slow, hot, waiting, relaxed. Pantomime before the first lines of conversation.)

35 Tempo I°

(People are arriving into the station.)

88

SOP.

he, he, he, he, he, he...

TEN.

There are

BAR.

You should set - tle down.

MEZZO

du.

Con - jo - vra las ma - li -

TEN.

lit - tle pa - per back books of ev - 'ry type a - vail - a - ble if you would

ka.

A - lim, me -

poco a poco cresc.

want them, on all sub - jects so it seems,__ and of

o - li - sti - to zon, bi -

⊕ Indicates segments not related to the preceding.

Is an-y-bod-y here from the group?

BAR.

do you look like some - bod - y? Here put on my hat -

ah - ha - say, no... you could look like

some - bod - y with that hat on -

BAR.

sub. *ff*   *meno f*

Look at that lit-tle boy__ o-ver there!   Is he   kick-ing his moth- er?

cresc. ed accel.

(Another man shakes his head.)   *f*   *allarg.*   *ff*

Well, per-haps he should be!   He,   he, he!

allarg.

43 Tempo I (♩.=48)

Piano *mf*   *f*   *mf*   (Cl., Trb.)

f   *appass.*

Str.

mf

mf   *f*   *mf*

f

mf

96

Pa, pa,——— pa, pa, pa, pa-up, pa, pa - rrrr...rp.

*In the textless passages, the singers may employ any appropriate
vocables they like, varying them to accord with the music.

It was my un-cle's who was a pro-fes-sion-al - -

which I am not.

As yet.

But _____ of which I am as - pir - ing to be.

59 Alla breve maestoso e pomposo (♩ = 88)

Subito meno mosso (♩ = 66)

I play the cor-net at wed-dings, par-ties,

danc-es, and pa - rades.

poco a poco cresc.

it is mine... it is mine...

poco a poco cresc.

61 Subito più mosso (♩ = 84-88)

(sempre cresc. al fine)

it is mine... it is mine...

it is mine... it is mine...

allargandosi

with lots of feath-ers like a bird's ___ nest? ___

you like hats ___ with lots of feath-ers like a bird's ___ nest? ___

No! ___

- dings? _____ ...at wed-dings? _____

- dings? _____ ...at wed-dings? _____

Oh! _____

Meno mosso (♩.=80)

Meno mosso (♩.=80)

65 Tempo I°

Oh! _____

Oh! _____

Oh! _____

65 Tempo I°

Say, is that a hat box, ma'm?— Ah!!—

Say, is that a hat box, ma'm?— Ah!!—

This is a hat box.

(Str.)

66 Stesso tempo ma vivacissimo

— Is that— a hat box!— Is that a

— Is that— a hat box!— Is that a

Yes, this is— a hat box!—

66 Stesso tempo ma vivacissimo

(Pno.)

per-fect-ly make box-es!...　　　box-es?　　Oh!

per-fect-ly make box-es!...　　　box-es?　　Oh!

I　　make...　　hats...　Oh!

70 Quasi cadenza (♩ = 44 ca.)

sotto voce

sotto voce

sotto voce

70 Quasi cadenza (♩ = 44 ca.)

(Cl.)

* The Mezzo's part, though **p**, should dominate this section.

71 Largo tranquillo (♩=40-42)

con dignità
p

I make hats _____ I make these hats for use when

71 Largo tranquillo (♩=40-42)

pp

(Vla.)

pp

sim.

an - y spe - cial hats are need-ed, I am of-ten called -- for mov-ies, I mean

(Vln.)

whenever they are making any special movies.

72 Tempo I°

Oh, _____ What are you called? What is your name?

Oh, _____ What are you called? What is your name?

72 Tempo I°

(Cl.)

(Pno.)

on an easel, the Conductor places a showcard bearing the following legend:)

"Souvenirs de Bayreuth"

* During the *Divertimento* the actors playing the puppets may perform various routines
(magician, juggler, snake-charmer, sword-swallower) or appropriate dances.

83 Stesso tempo

poco a poco cresc.

[85] Stesso tempo
molto ritmico

* About 30-45 seconds: an ad lib. percussion solo featuring clichés of the period (1914-1920) and additional instruments such as horns and whistles associated with vaudeville routines.

** Throughout this final section of the *Divertimento*, the violin and viola should make free use of sub-semitonal intonation, particularly to replace half steps with quarter-tones in trills and other appropriate passages.

94 Pesante (♩ = 63)

BAR.

You'd think a per-son could trav-el light-er than this, _____ ten suits, _____ shoes... _____ shoes!!! _____ Whew! (Whistling.) *a piacere*

158

(He 'listens' to one of the cardboard figures.)

spe - cial suit - case

made to car - ry shoes.

Has lit - tle cloth pock - ets in - side for hold - ing the

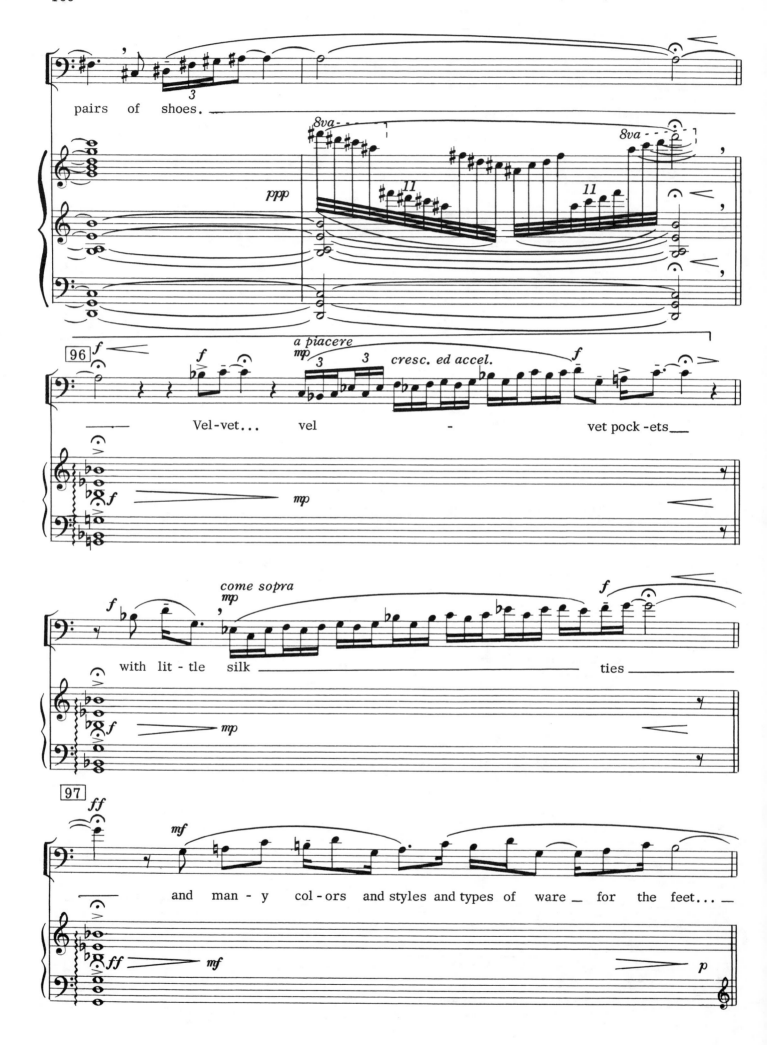

pairs of shoes. ____

ppp

a piacere

96 *f* *f* *mp* 3 3 *cresc. ed accel.* *f*

Vel-vet... vel - vet pock -ets___

f *mp*

come sopra *mp*

f *f*

with lit - tle silk _____ ties _____

f *mp*

97 *ff* *mf*

and man - y col -ors and styles and types of ware __ for the feet... __

ff *mf* *p*

shoes with glass heels, real ex - pen - sive slip-pers lined with

fuzz... _____ or vel

- vet, vel - vet ____ or silk.. _____

bat should chase a la-dy... I've— got boots with brooms for la-dy bats, and that's no

joke... you should see them... ___

can you see them? ___ eh? ___

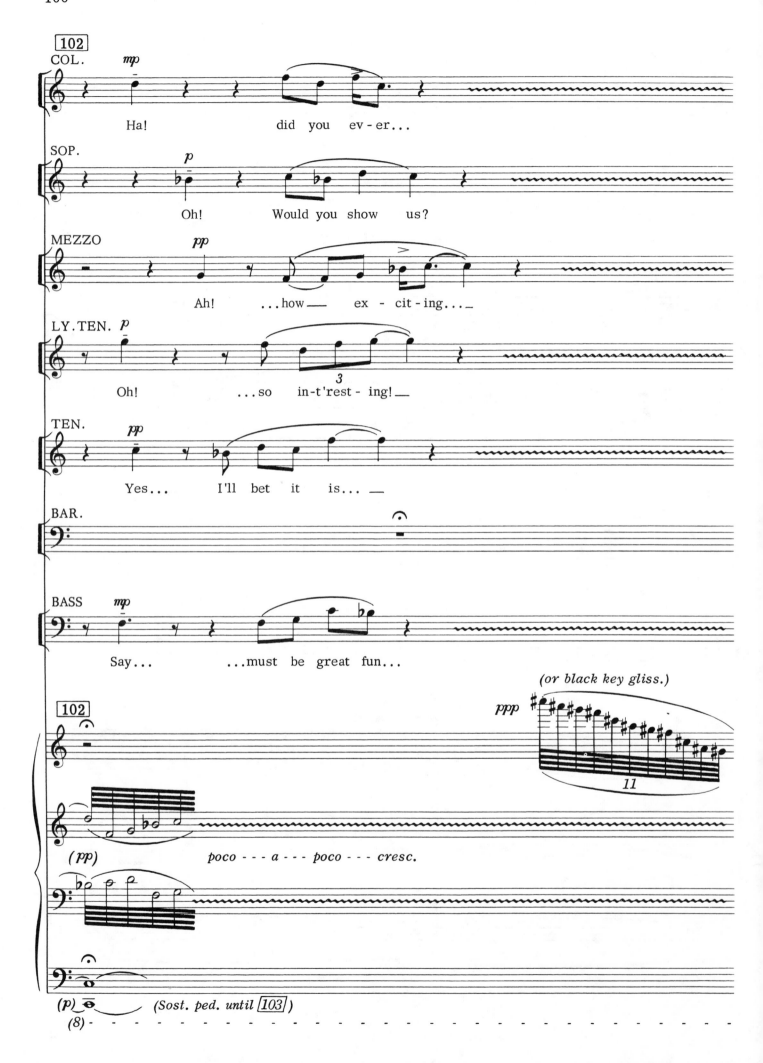

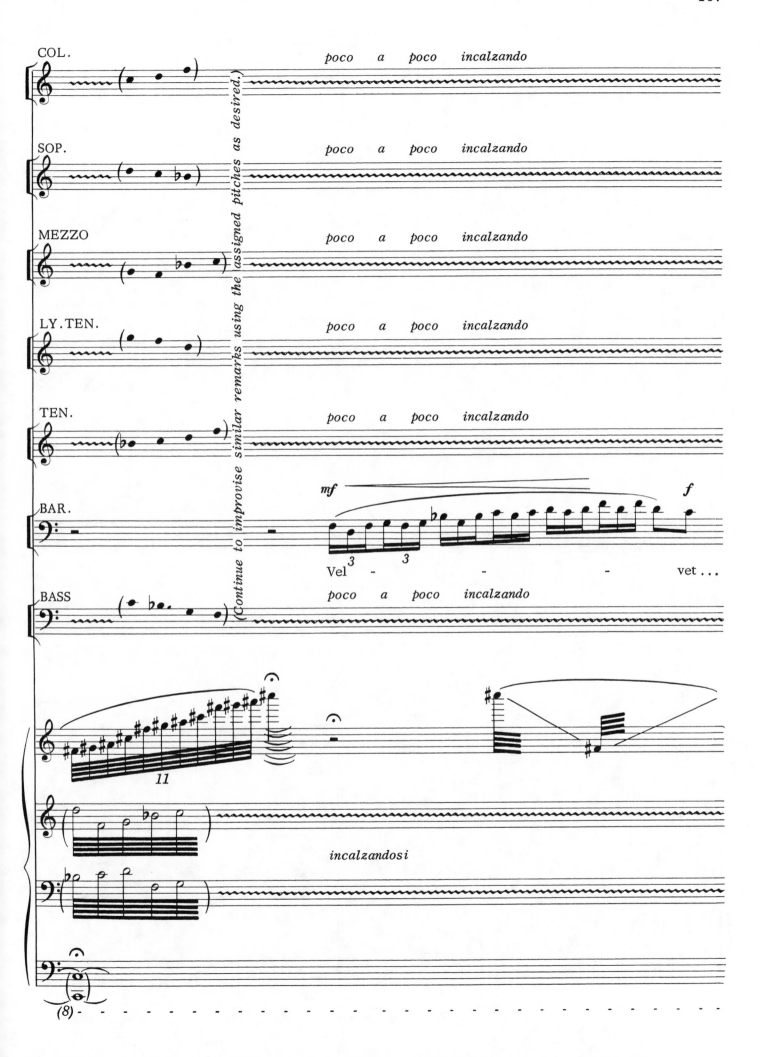

168

(black key gliss.)

(The ladies flutter around him grabbing at the latch of his case. One of them tugs at the suitcase.)

COL. O let me see. Do let me see. Do you have a pair for me?

SOP. me see._ Do let me see. Do you have a pair for me?

MEZZO let me see them. Do you have a pair for me?

(He slaps her hand very hard, reminiscent of puppets hitting.
For a moment they resemble the puppets in a show somewhere.)

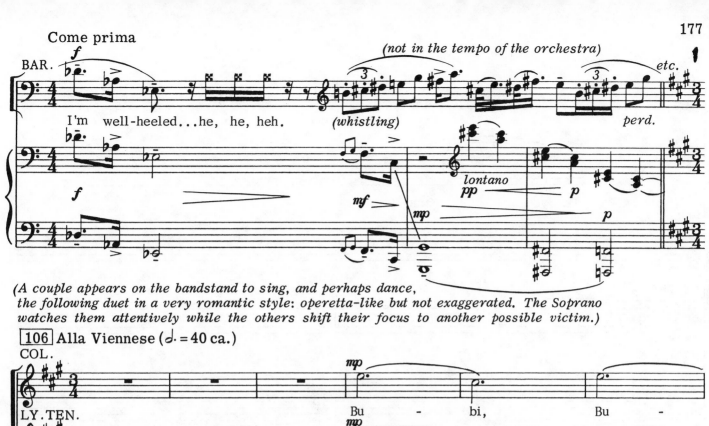

180

(No answer. She changes seat. The couple disappears.)

192

SOP. *p*

love - ly__ la - dy?_____ Like__ some dis-tant mu - sic... some

TEN. *p*

spoke__ so__ sweet - ly... Like some dis - tant mu - sic... to__

poco cresc.

rall. - - - - - - Largamente (♩ = 44 ca.)

SOP. *poco cresc.* *mp* *sub.* *pp*

wind....__ some tune,__ some dis - tant cry..._____

TEN. *poco cresc.* *rall.* *mp* *sub. pp*

__ his love - ly la - dy_____ he spoke so sweet - ly._____

COL. *rall.* *pppp*

Komm'__

(The operetta couple reappears.)

LY. TEN. *rall.* *pppp*

Komm'__

rall. - - - - - - Largamente (♩ = 44 ca.)

mp

* A fermata lunga for Sop. and Tenor alone; then another fermata lunga as Col. and
Ly. Ten. enter imperceptibly and slowly match the dynamic level of the others.

SOP. *sempre diminuendo e rall.*

danc - ing... we may go danc - ing... we may go danc - ing... we may go

TEN. *sempre diminuendo e rall.*

danc - ing... we may go danc - ing... we may go danc - ing... we may go

sempre diminuendo e rall.

129 Molto adagio (♩ = 52)

p possibile *a niente*

danc-ing... we may go danc-ing... we may go danc - ing...

danc-ing... we may go danc-ing... we may go danc - ing...

129 Molto adagio (♩ = 52)

(Vln.)

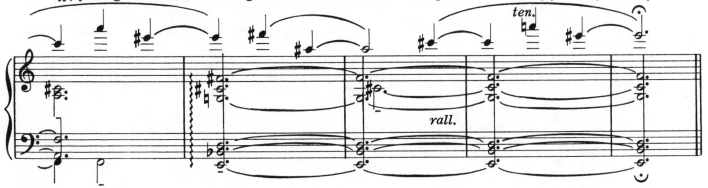

(He kisses her softly. She looks at him suddenly as if none of the above had occurred. If she is grateful for his understanding she cannot or does not show it and simply fans herself and gazes off, putting one hand on her bag. All watch Mr. Owen as he goes to the bishop for confession.)

206

and a flag stretched___ out

sfz -mf   *sim.*

(*f*)

o - pen hand - ed... _____

134 Mosso e giubiloso (♩. = 76)

ff   *f*

___ it___ was the col - or____ of the blank-et on my bed.___

ff ____ *f*

sailed _____ a - bove the hol - ly - hocks, _____

141 Cominciando nello stesso tempo

and I rushed un-dressed, na-ked through the

kitch - en pan- try _____ to the o - cean floor __ and I

wait,___ but my sail - ors nev - er called a - gain...

my sail - ors nev - er,_____ nev - er, nev - er called a - gain...

I head toward the sea now_____ with my paint box.

147 Alla breve (♩ = 84)

LY. TEN.

What kind?_

BASS

(This aria should be sung with a foreign accent, perhaps Slavic.)

Pup-pets - pup-pets - sure ___

147 Alla breve (♩ = 84)

(Pno., Sax., Trb.)

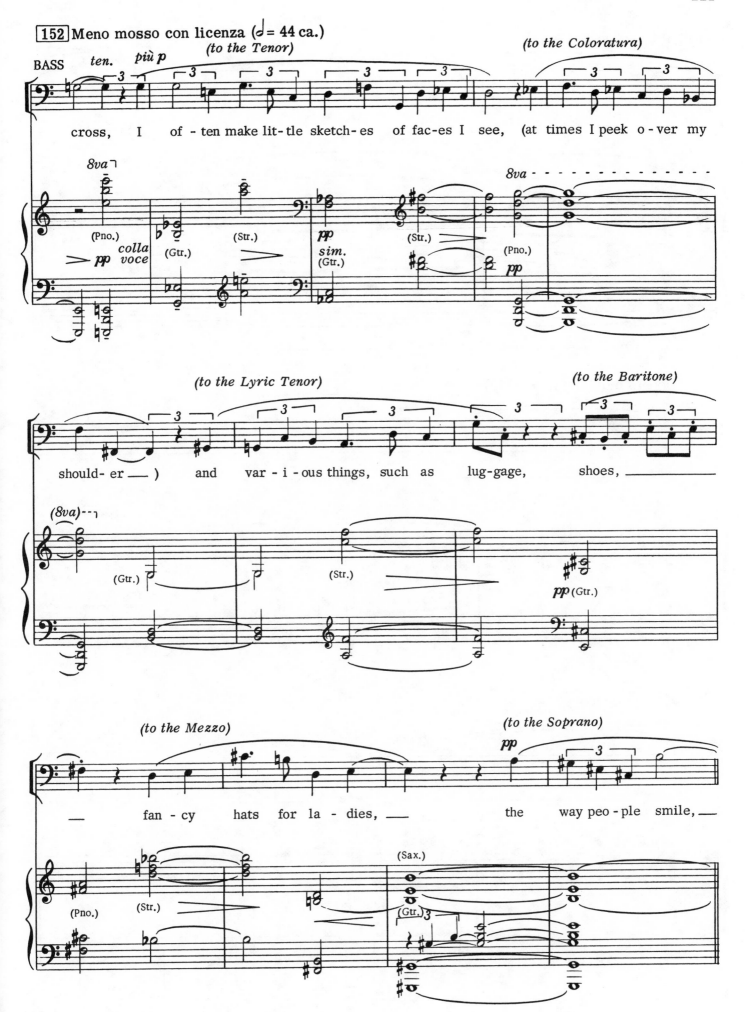

222

(No answer. And the next time we see the man he is across the station as if he had never spoken to anyone, looking out a window or speaking to a cardboard figure in deep conversation.)

* The tempo of this passacaglia, while deliberate, must never become rigid: a gradual accelera-
tion up to the twice-as-fast tempo of [170] is indicated throughout as a general scheme only.

know-   but nev - er mind   me.

159

And   this   is   your   paint   kit,

(Vln.)

mp   *poco a poco cresc.*

(Cl., Trb.)

TEN.

Yes.

BAR.

eh?   May   I

(Pno.)

mf   *ancora cresc.*

be - ing as I am a trav - el - ler I've lit-tle touch with art.

TEN.

BAR.

Brush - es, no doubt. _____

What? ___

Brush - es, to paint with.

I'm out of most of my tubes right now, ___ I've used up a lot of my paint late-ly...

But you must have some

Oh, yes, oh, yes! ___

paints... ___

234

236

* All trills whole-step.

no! _____ Let me see YOUR stuff - -

167 Più mosso (♩.= 92) *sempre poco a poco cresc. ed accel.*

have ___ a pup - pet show.... ___ that's

167 Più mosso (♩.= 92) *sempre poco a poco cresc. ed accel.*

bet-ter than a pic-ture. Would ev-'ry-bod-y like to see a

pup-pet or a dum-my? Some fan - cy ____

shoes, Let ____ me see your lov - er.

See a pup - pet or a dum - my, a dum - my, a dum - my...

168 Feroce (♩. = 96)
non legato

does - n't he have some in - t'rest - ing lug - gage?

168 Feroce (♩. = 96)

ff   *sfz*   *sfz*

sfz

...why don't you play your cor - net?

sfz

...see a pup-pet or a dum-my, or a

170 Deciso (♩.= 104) *(All are climbing up on the trunks to pose, smiling and remarking ad lib.)*

COL.
parlato **ff**
Now where did I put that mirror, etc...

SOP.
parlato **ff**
Is my hair all in place, etc...

MEZZO
parlato **ff**
This should really be something, etc...

LY. TEN.
parlato **ff**
Come on, everybody, etc...

TEN.
dum - my...

BAR.
parlato **ff**
Don't forget my shoes, etc...

BASS
parlato **ff**
Let me help you up, etc...

170 Deciso (♩.= 104)

(Long pantomime of moving to strike a pose.)

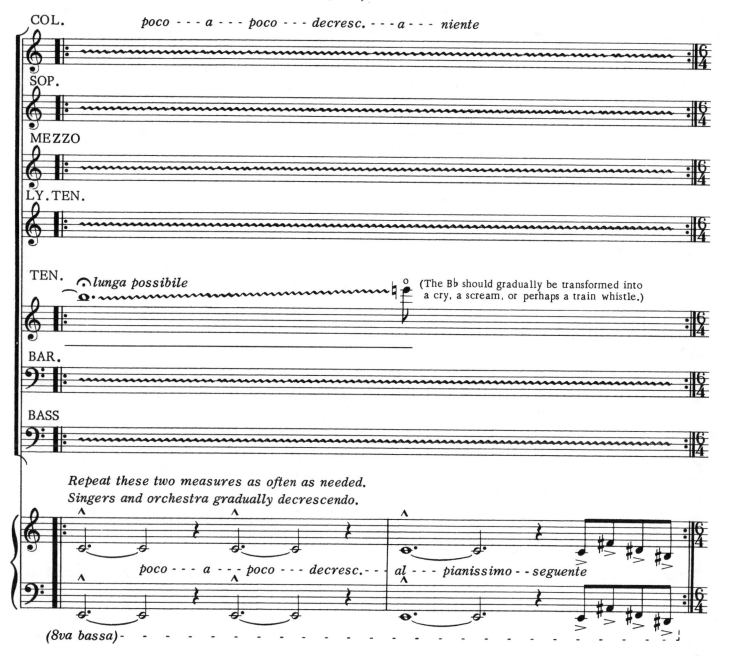

(Mr. Owen with his box...

They pose — Mr. Owen is trapped and confused.

He opens his paint box which is completely empty...

The lid flops down...   pantomime...

He stands there...   The others continue to pose and grin.)

Doppio movimento (♩. = ○. del prec.)

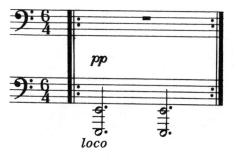

*Repeat this measure as often
as needed, always pianissimo.*

(Mr. Owen's paint box lid continues to flap back and forth.)

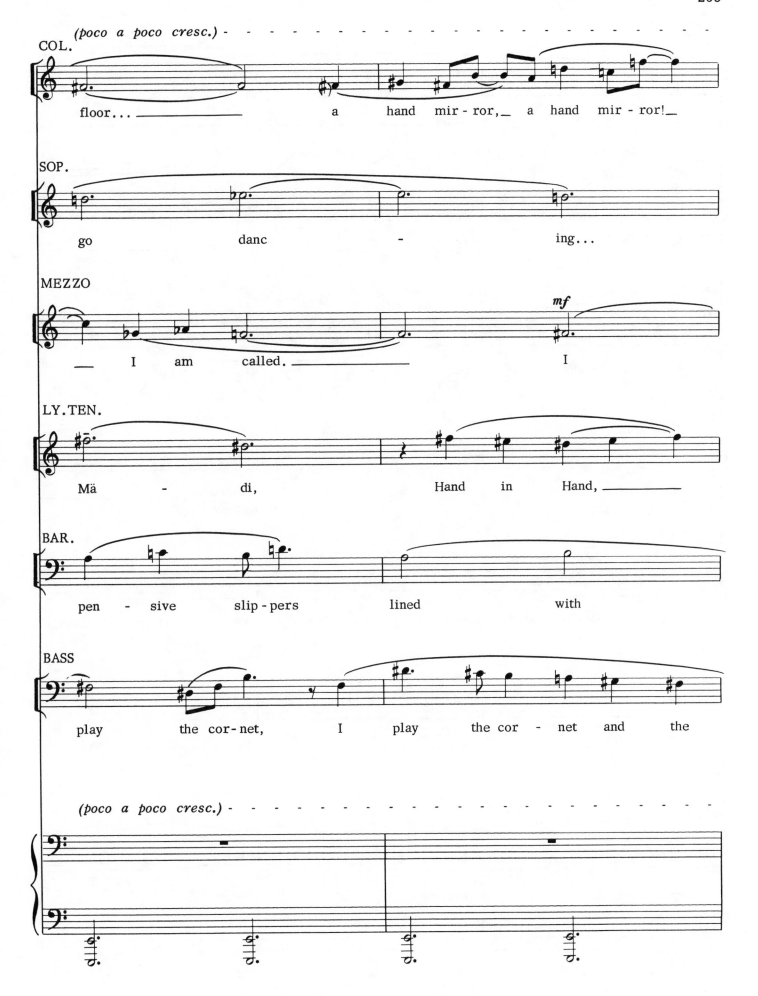

254

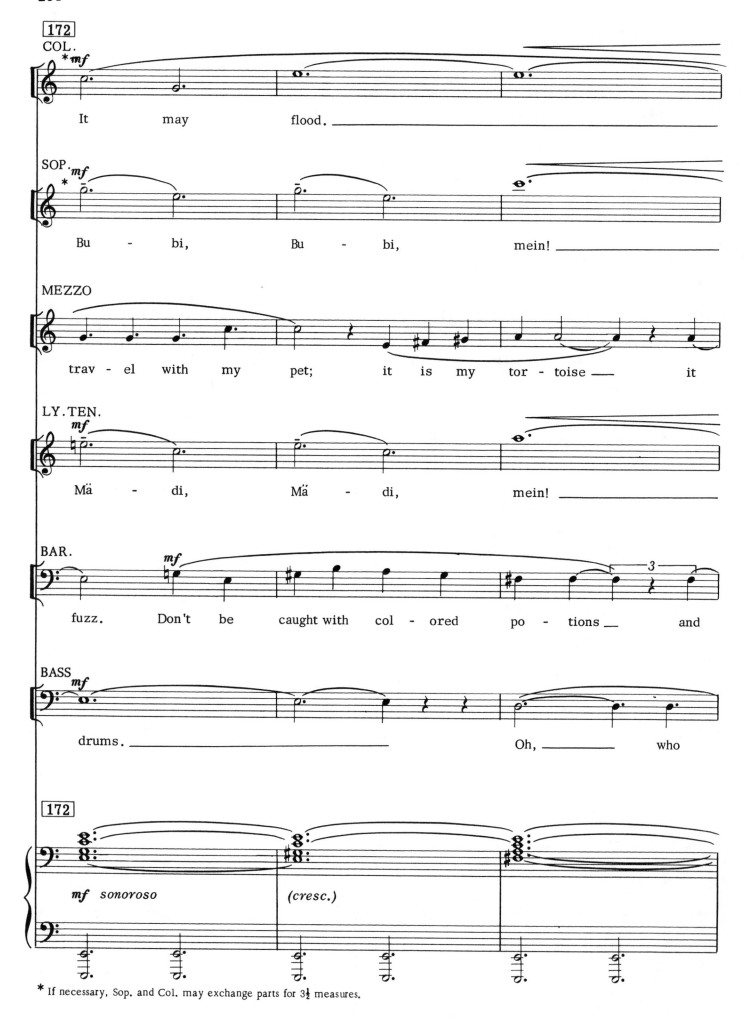

* If necessary, Sop. and Col. may exchange parts for 3½ measures.

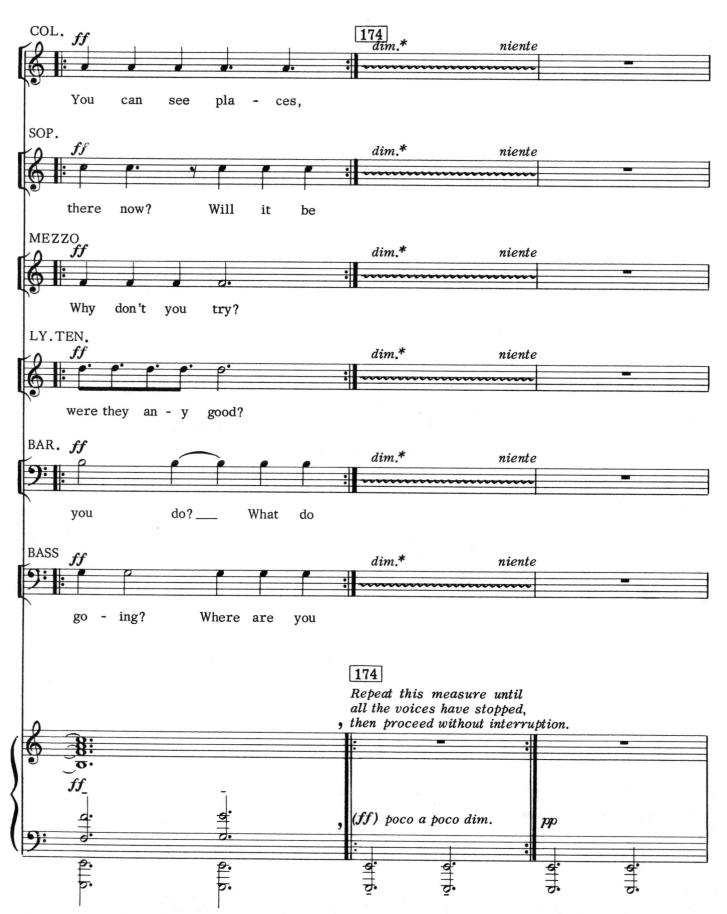

* The preceding measure to be repeated as often as needed; the singing should be gradually transformed into speech, (resembling the indistinct, toneless muttering at the beginning of the opera) and the tempo varied in each part.

(There is a suspended moment. Then all viewing shifts focus to the puppet play which is about to start.)

(Mr. Owen remains suspended in the earlier moment.)

175 Doppio movimento (♩.= 104) (come prima)

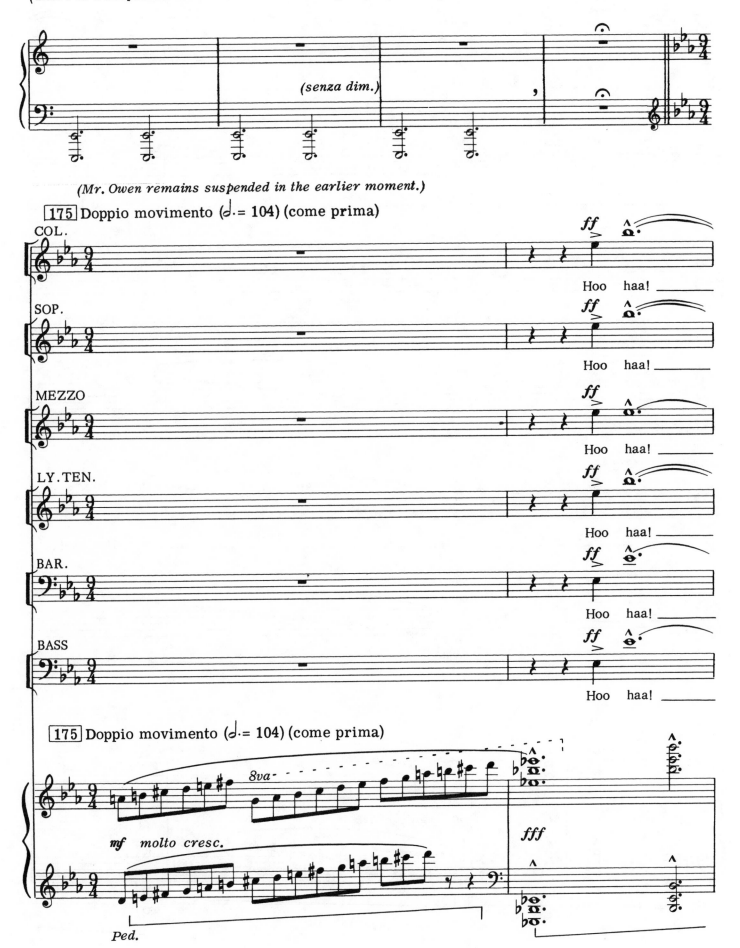

COL. ... Hoo haa! ____

SOP. ... Hoo haa! ____

MEZZO ... Hoo haa! ____

LY.TEN. ... Hoo haa! ____

BAR. ... Hoo haa! ____

BASS ... Hoo haa! ____

175 Doppio movimento (♩.= 104) (come prima)

260

(The puppet action resumes.)

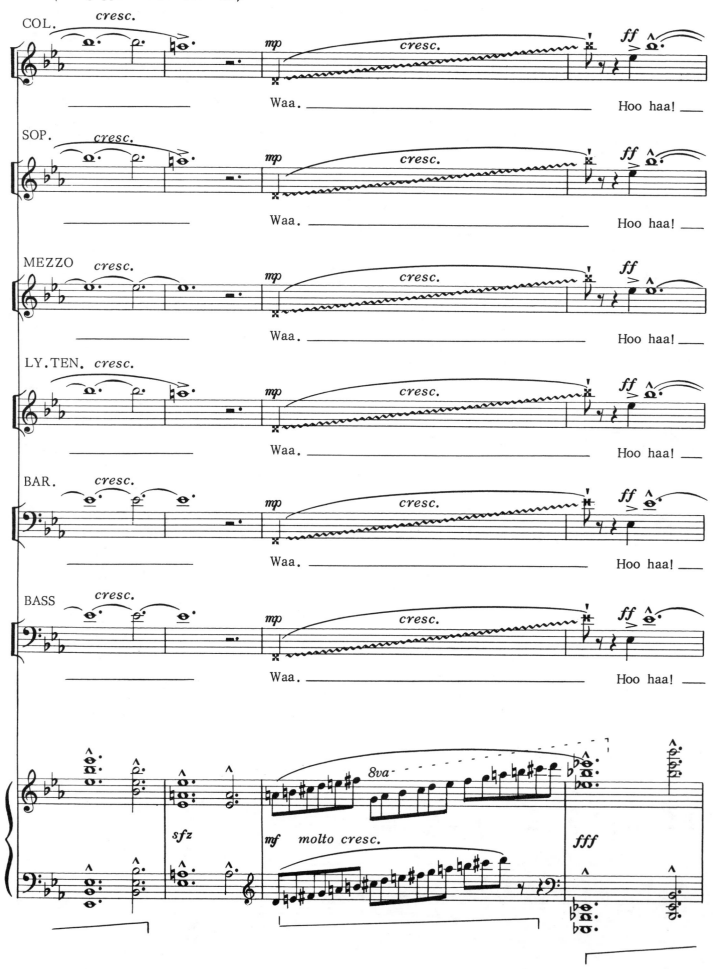

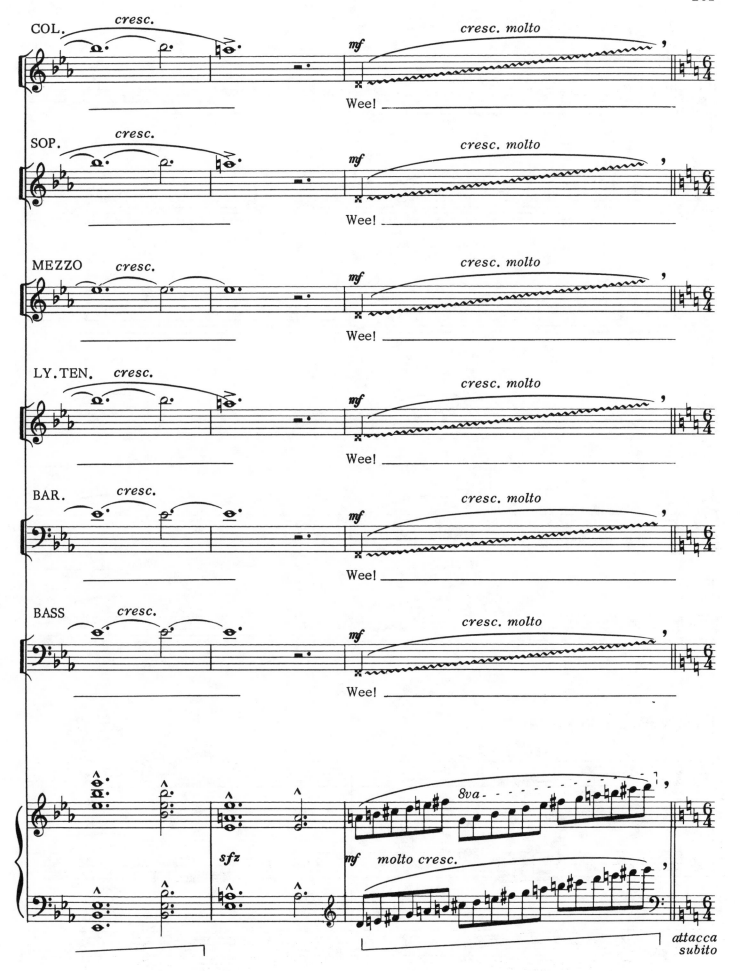

262

(One puppet smashes the other into the floor....

The other raises a victorious board.
The onlookers applaud the winner.)

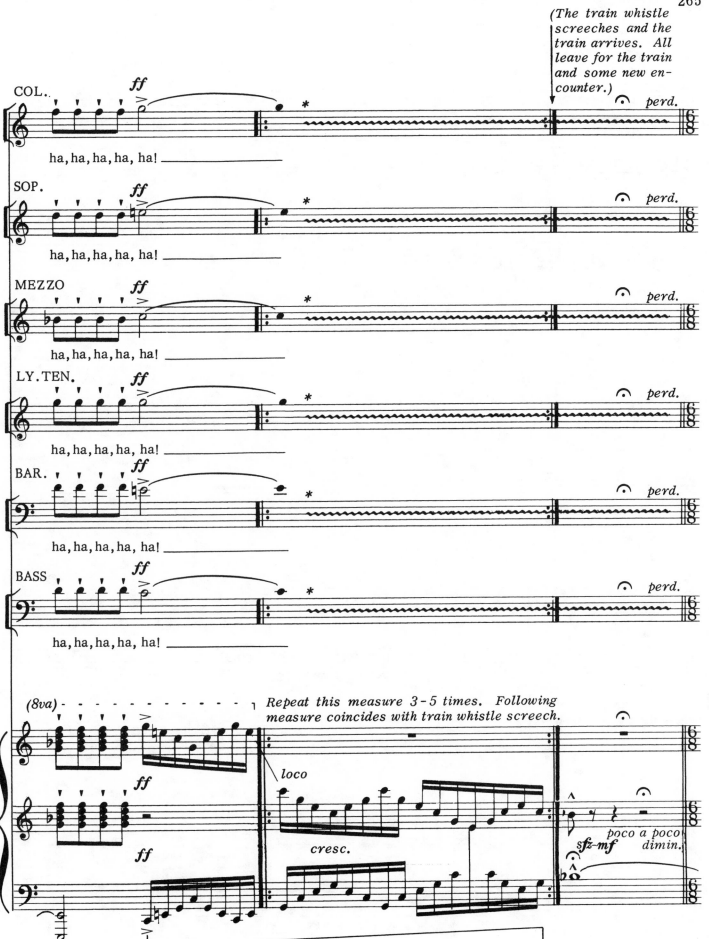

(The train whistle screeches and the train arrives. All leave for the train and some new encounter.)

COL. ff
ha, ha, ha, ha, ha!

SOP. ff
ha, ha, ha, ha, ha!

MEZZO ff
ha, ha, ha, ha, ha!

LY. TEN. ff
ha, ha, ha, ha, ha!

BAR. ff
ha, ha, ha, ha, ha!

BASS ff
ha, ha, ha, ha, ha!

perd.

(8va)

Repeat this measure 3-5 times. Following measure coincides with train whistle screech.

loco

ff

cresc.

sfz-mf

poco a poco dimin.

* Ad lib. sung remarks and laughter until exit.

(. . . All but Mr. Owen and the puppet.

178 Adagio mesto (♪ = 80 ca.)
con stanchezza

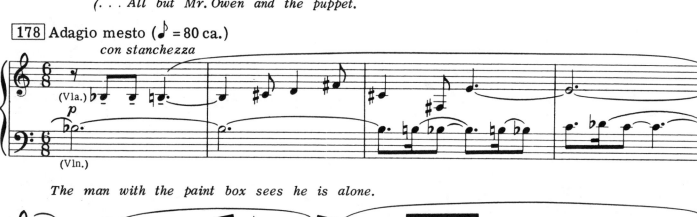

The man with the paint box sees he is alone.

179
molto calmo

He slowly moves toward the puppet stage...

180 (Gtr.)

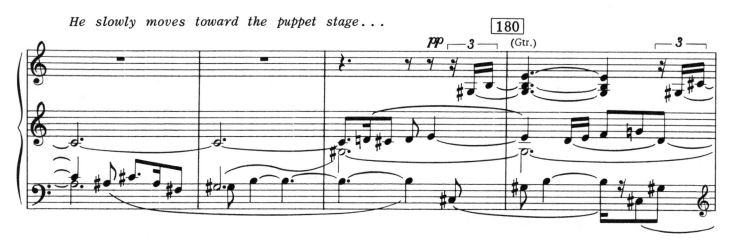

poco - - a - - poco - - cresc. - - ma - - senza - - accel. - - - - - -

...and climbs onto it and,

becoming semi-puppetlike, begins to act out the boat story with the other puppet.)

181 Molto agitato (♩ = 112)

(He is the Captain.)

182 Scorrevole (♩. = 66–69)

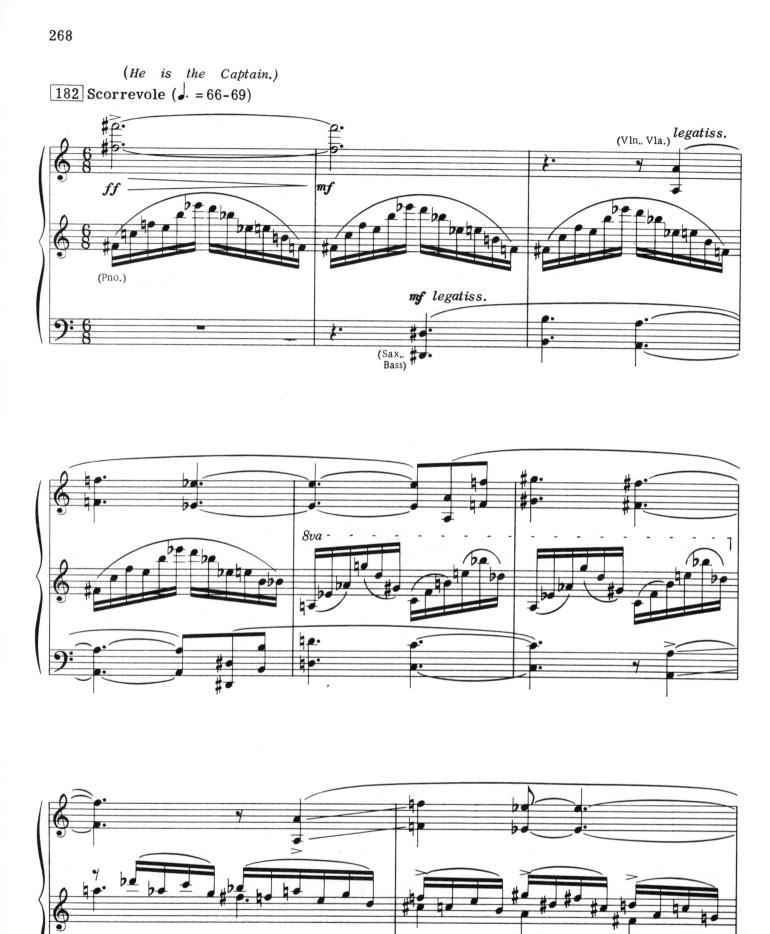

(*A puppet ship materializes.*)

183 Stesso tempo ($\.{d}. = \.{d}.$)

(Mr. Owen, now the captain of the ship, sings his lament.)
TEN.
([184]-[185] is sung through a megaphone.)

[184] Recit., a piacere   in tempo

All hands, all hands,_____

[184] Recit., colla voce

in tempo

move quick-ly, move quick-ly to your cap-tain's call. ___

Now hear me, my men, ___ and lis-ten well. ___

185 Largamente cantabile (♩ = 50-52)

(il canto sempre rapsodico, con licenza)

___ We sail this sum-mer morn-ing, set sail this

272

* This undulating figure, Bb - A, barely audible, is to be played freely, i.e., not synchronized with the principal tempo. From time to time, it may fade away completely and then return.

fear. The boat is mag - i - cal, made out of glass

and ice. We'll sail through fire and clouds. We'll an - chor

in a flow - er's bell.

The birds will guide us home. Their wings will be our sails, for

this is my ship, my ship, I'm

188 Come prima ma poco meno mosso
e calmo possibile (♪ = 116)

cap - tain of this mag - ic ship.

276

*The off-stage voices come from a great distance, barely audible at first but gradually drawing nearer.

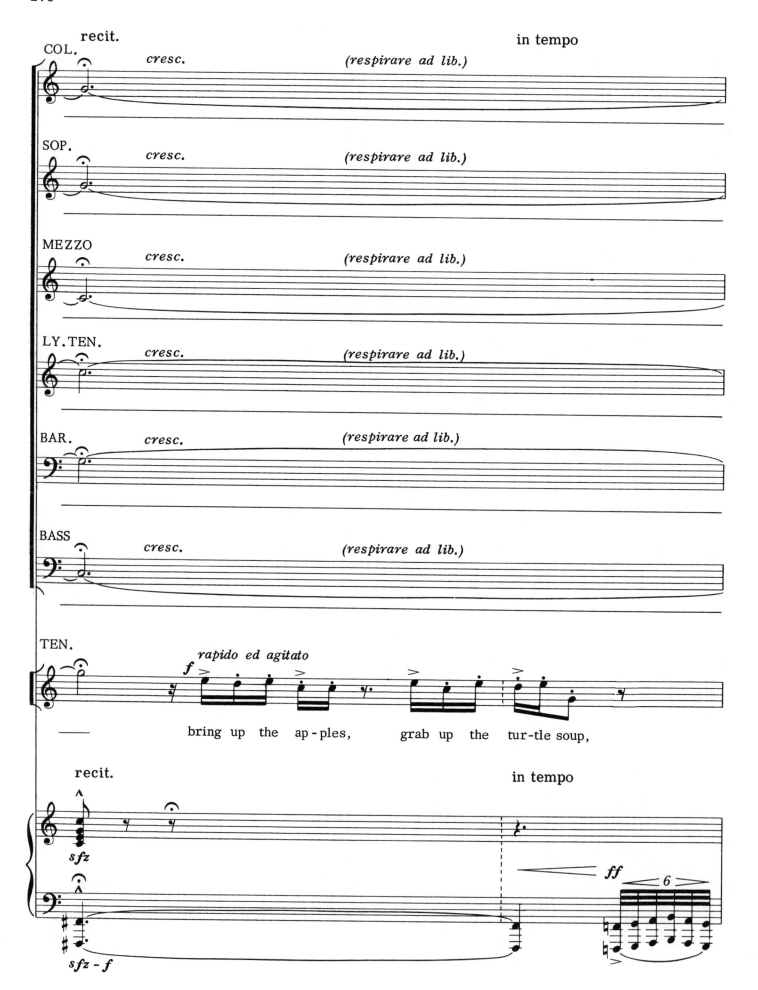

... and slowly moves off into the distance with him and the puppet in it.)

H - weee _____

H - weee _____

H - weee _____

H - weee _____

H - weee _____

H - weee _____

283

* The duration of this passage should be determined by the
capacities of the singers and wind instruments: as long as possible.

284

* Continue alternation of the two pitches, slowly and irregularly,
  not in tempo nor together. Stagger breathing. Individual
  voices should emerge briefly, then subside.

288

(The boat disappears entirely.)

(The puppet stage curtains close.)

195 Stesso tempo (♩ = ♩. del prec.)

rit.

(cominciare impercettibilmente)
(vln.) *ppp*

196 Languido, come prima (♩ = 42 ca.)

(The cardboard creatures in the station jerk and jazz their way out and across.)

197 Pochino meno mosso (♩ = 40 ca.)

rall. al fine

198

delicato ma distinto

(Pno.)

(hold until
all sound dies)

Fine dell'opera

MAROC: La gare de Shamula
MOROCCO: Railway Station of Shamula
MAROK: Bahnhof von Shamula
MAROCCO: Stazione di Shamula

Dear Friends,

     We travel all over together, we visit places, we take photograph of the places we visit .... of our costumes ... with children. We visit temples and churches and in a plaza we fed the birds and put our shoes in the water. I was given blue flowers ... we went on tiptoe through fog. when we get off the train next time we may go dancing.

               Your loving.
                 C.B.